May our children grow up in peace and let them explore the miracles of this world.

Let's begin the journey...

This book belongs to:

_____

2nd Edition 2021
ISBN Paperback: 978-3-949304-02-6
ISBN Hardcover: 978-3-949304-03-3

Dear Parents and Little Explorers,

this book comes with a <u>free</u> digital bonus which contains the **soundscapes** accompanying the story plus **fun coloring pages**.

Ask your parents to download this <u>free</u> bonus at:

www.jolaswittler.com/trucks

Your friend,
Jolas

Who's starting early on the road?
The dump truck hauls its heavy load.

The mixer truck stops on the street
to spin its drum and form concrete.

The excavator that is clear,
is digging holes for this site here!

And who can move this heavy stack?
The forklift can, but please step back!

Most cranes are tall. Just look up high!
They lift their loads into the sky.

The firefighters rush around.
Their siren makes a screaming sound.

The fire engine drives through town.
'Cause there's a fire. Don't slow down!

They're just in time. There is no doubt.
They'll soon have put the fire out.

And if you're lost in town one day,
an officer will know the way.

An officer stops anyone
who speeds through town with belt undone.

Oh no! Look, here! Two cars have crashed.
The driver's hurt. The cars are smashed.

At the garage, a crafty man repairs a rusty broken van.

The car wash makes your car so clean.
The dirt has gone. It's sparkling green.

A service station's on the way,
to refuel cars that drove all day.

The garbage truck drives without haste
all through the town to pick up waste.

When night sets in, it's getting dark,
and trash collectors clean the park.

Did you notice?

1.) Do you know all these vehicles? What are they doing?

2.) Did you spot these animals? Where are they?

3.) There is a cat in every picture! Did you spot them all?

And while all children are asleep,
the streets get cleaned with care – sweep sweep.

Thank you for reading this book!
If you enjoyed it, we would be so grateful for an online review.

Impressum

CURIOUS WORLD
BOOKS

Curious World Books
Tobias Ebel
Wilhelm-Stein-Weg 2
22339 Hamburg
Germany

© 2021 Jolas Wittler All Rights Reserved.
Illustrated by Kama Towcik
2nd Edition 2021

ISBN Paperback: 978-3-949304-02-6
ISBN Hardcover: 978-3-949304-03-3
E-Book: available without ISBN
MP3-Audiobook: downloadable www.jolaswittler.com/soundbook
   Want to contact the author? Email to jo@jolaswittler.com. Follow me on Instagram or Facebook.

Bonus Offer

We have a special gift for you!

Ask your parents to download the "Vehicles
of the Town" activity pack containing the
accompanying **soundscapes** and **coloring
pages** for <u>free</u>!

www.jolaswittler.com/vehicles

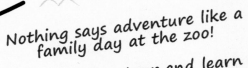

Explore more!

Nothing says adventure like a family day at the zoo!

Join this fun tour and learn about the creatures we share this world with!

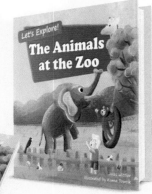

The Animals at the Zoo

ISBN (paperback): 978-3-949304-10-1
ISBN (hardcover): 978-3-949304-11-8

To support early multi-lingual learning "The Vehicles of the Town" is also available in these languages:

In Spanish (latin) / en español (latino)
Title: ¡Exploremos! Vehículos en la ciudad
ISBN: 978-3-949304-04-0 (Paperback)
ISBN: 978-3-949304-05-7 (Hardcover)

In French / en français
Title: Explorons ! Les véhicules de la ville
ISBN: 978-3-949304-06-4 (Paperback)
ISBN: 978-3-949304-07-1 (Hardcover)

In German / auf deutsch
Title: Wir entdecken! Die Fahrzeuge in der Stadt
ISBN: 978-3-949304-00-2 (Paperback)
ISBN: 978-3-949304-01-9 (Hardcover)